MW00624639

Your Financial Revolution

THE POWER OF ALLEGIANCE

GARY KEESEE

Your Financial Revolution: The Power of Allegiance Workbook

Copyright © 2018 by Gary Keesee.

Unless otherwise noted, all Scriptures are taken from the New International Version® (NIV)® of the Holy Bible. Copyright © 1973, 1978, 1984 by Biblica, Inc.™ All rights reserved worldwide.

Scripture quotations taken from the Amplified® Bible, Copyright © 2015 by The Lockman Foundation. All rights reserved.

Scripture quotations taken from the New Living Translation of the Holy Bible. Copyright © 1996, 2004, 2015 by Tyndale House Foundation. Used by permission of Tyndale House Publishers, Inc., Carol Stream, Illinois 60188. All rights reserved.

Printed in the United States of America. All rights reserved under International Copyright Law. Contents and/or cover may not be reproduced in whole or in part in any form without the express written consent of the Publisher.

ISBN: 978-1-945930-10-2

Published by Free Indeed Publishers.
Distributed by Faith Life Now.

Faith Life Now
P.O. 779
New Albany, OH 43054
1-(888)-391-LIFE

You can reach Faith Life Now Ministries on the Internet at www.faithlifenow.com.

CONTENTS

QUESTIONS:
Fill in the blanks from your reading.

SCRIPTURES:
Dive into the Word of God.

THOUGHTS:
Respond to these prompts to go deeper.

KNOW THIS:
Meditate on these important standout statements.

PRAYER

INTRODUCTION

THIS CAN COMPLETELY CHANGE YOUR LIFE.

Answers.

Friend, there are answers in the Kingdom of God—answers that work the same for *anyone* and *everyone* who will take the time to learn them and apply them.

For years now, I've wanted to put into writing the journey that God took Drenda and me on. I've shared parts of our story in letters and in teachings, but God told me it was time to write a series of books that told it all—all of the good, the bad, and the ugly details of our story, and the stories of others—in a series that will help people understand the mysteries of His Kingdom and experience real change in their lives just like we did.

This is the first study in that series. I started with this one because, although there are many Kingdom principles that are part of living a successful life, I knew this one was the most significant. Because if I could only share ONE principle with you, it would be the power of allegiance.

Know this: this isn't another study on finances.

This study is a *journey*—a journey of discovery about the Kingdom of God that is available to you right now and can completely transform your life just like it completely transformed mine.

This study is also a call for a REVOLUTION—a *revolt* against the kingdom of darkness and the system designed to confine you to a life of survival and fear.

Because you should be living out your God-designed destiny, a life full of purpose, passion, and hope for your future.

You should be experiencing the promises of God in every area of your life.

What are you waiting for?

We have some work to do. Let's go.

> *His divine power has given us everything we need for life and godliness through our knowledge of him who called us by his own glory and goodness.*
>
> –2 Peter 1:3

CHAPTER 1
THE KINGDOM

ALLEGIANCE [ə'lējəns] – the loyalty of a citizen to his or her government or of a subject to his or her sovereign; commitment and devotion in the firmest sense; faithfulness; obedience

Do Not Learn to Live with Fear

Stress does some things to you. Not only can it cause you severe physical symptoms, but also it opens the door to fear in your life. And fear opens doors to as many of its terrible friends as possible—demonic influences, confusion, depression, and more.

Unresolved ________________ ____________ and ____________ ____________ make living with fear a way of life.

You must not learn to live, or cope, with fear.

What financial issues are unresolved in your life right now?

KNOW THIS: THERE ARE ANSWERS. YOU CAN BE FREE.

Isaiah 61:1 talks of sharing the "good news" with the poor.

Good news to a poor man is that he can be _________.

In what ways do you recognize that financial stress has been taking a toll on your life?

Write out Philippians 4:19:

What are your needs right now?

KNOW THIS: GOD WANTS YOU TO UNDERSTAND HOW HIS KINGDOM OPERATES. HE WANTS YOU TO BE FREE.

As a believer, you can love God, go to church, tithe, and be on your way to heaven, but you MUST learn how to bring the power and authority of the Kingdom into your life to affect your natural ______________________.

Understanding the Kingdom

God's Kingdom is not a democracy; it is a kingdom with a King.

The _________________ of the King flows down through the Kingdom with ________________ authority through various government offices and people who operate under that authority.

A kingdom is a group of people who are held together by law or ______________________.

Isaiah 9:6-7 say:

> *For to us a child is born, to us a son is given, and the ____________________ will be on his shoulders. And he will be called Wonderful Counselor, Mighty God, Everlasting Father, Prince of Peace.*
>
> *Of the ____________ ___ ______ ________________ and peace there will be no end. He will reign on David's throne and over ______ ________________, establishing and upholding it with justice and righteousness from that time on and forever. The zeal of the Lord Almighty will accomplish this.*

_____________________ is the head of this government.

KNOW THIS: WHEN YOU ACCEPTED JESUS AS YOUR PERSONAL SAVIOR, YOU BECAME A PART OF HIS GOVERNMENT; YOU BECAME A CITIZEN OF THE KINGDOM OF GOD.

Read this prayer, adapted from John 1:12-13, aloud:

> *Thank You, Jesus, that because I have received You, and believed in Your name, that You have given me the legal right to become a child of God.*

Ephesians 2:19 says you are not only a citizen of the Kingdom of God but also a member of His very own _______________, a son or daughter of the King.

Sons and Daughters of God	Citizens of His Kingdom
• Secure • Access to the entire estate • Coheir with Jesus (Romans 8:17) • Honor • Authority • Assurance	• Legal rights and benefits within His government, made known to us by His Word, the Bible • Access to justice—enforcement and administration of Kingdom law (His precious promises) • Laws do not change = complete confidence and security • Same rights for all, no respecter of persons (Acts 10:34)

God's Kingdom is established and upheld through _________________________, the administration of His law.

To ensure that you have what God says is right within His Kingdom, what is legally yours as a citizen in that Kingdom, God has given you access to justice—the process or ________________ that you will have what He has promised you.

Jesus is the guarantee.

Second Corinthians 2:20 clearly says that every promise is "Yes" and "Amen."

ALL of the promises of God are for you. It has already been decided; it is ____________ yours.

Once you learn what God says is *legally* yours as a citizen of His Kingdom, you need to learn how to *legally* lay claim to what is *legally* yours and release it in the earth realm.

List three promises from the Word of God that you know you have yet to legally claim as yours as a citizen of the Kingdom of God:

1. ____
   ____

2. ____
   ____

3. ____
   ____

KNOW THIS: KINGDOMS OPERATE BY LAWS AND LAWS DO NOT CHANGE. YOU CAN LEARN THEM, APPLY THEM, AND HAVE THE BENEFIT OF THEM OPERATING IN YOUR LIFE.

If you know the law of God's Kingdom (His will), and you know that you have access to justice—the process of enforcement that guarantees you what the law says—then you can be confident and not ____________.

First John 5:14 says, "*This is the* ________________ *we have in approaching God: that if we ask anything according to his will, he hears us.*"

Do you believe God hears you when you pray? ________________

How is this chapter changing the way you've viewed God and His Kingdom?

Write out 2 Peter 1:3:

Notice that 2 Peter 1:3 is *past tense*. God has *already* provided everything you need for life and godliness. Every one of His promises is for you.

Luke 6:20b says, "*Blessed are you who are poor, for yours is the kingdom of God.*"

This tells you that your answer for your finances is His ____________________. Knowing how to tap into the laws of the Kingdom here in the earth realm, just as Jesus did, is your answer.

If you don't understand spiritual laws, you won't have the ability to enjoy their benefit or to ____________________ them when you need them.

Do you believe you are truly committed to learning God's system? Why or why not?

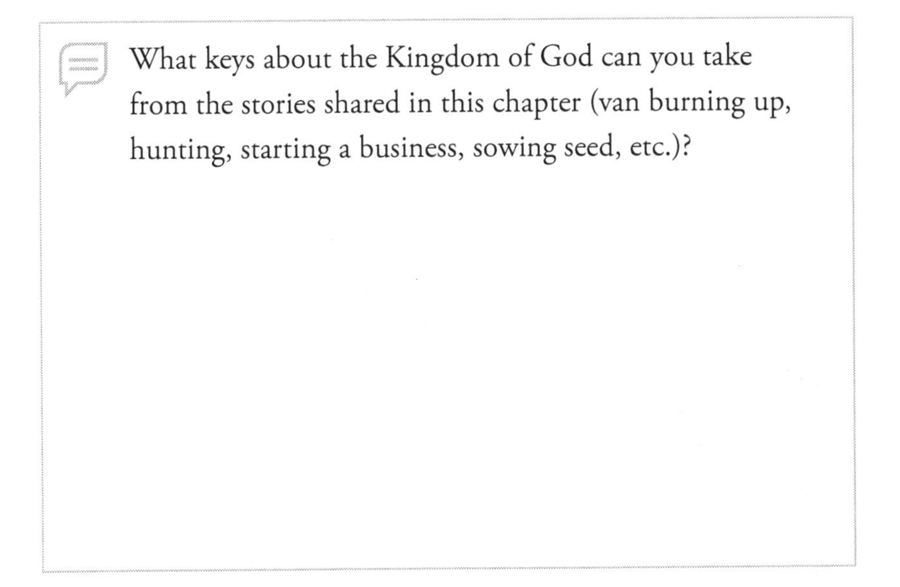

Affirming Your Allegiance — Seek Him First

Matthew 6:33 tells you to "*Seek FIRST his kingdom and his righteousness, and all these things will be given to you as well.*"

Be intentional this week to seek the Kingdom of God first. Don't just try to *find* time. *Make* time. Life will never slow down unless you make it. There will always be distractions. And Satan will keep using one of his best tactics—keeping you "too busy" to spend time with God—as long as you let him.

Prioritize prayer, reading and studying His Word, and listening to teachings. Keep God and His Word at the forefront of your thoughts. Ask Him to help you to really be a "spiritual scientist" as you read His Word, and to reveal to you how His Kingdom operates, your rights as a citizen, and how you can legally claim what is already legally yours. Be sure you take notes!

“

Lord, I praise You that You are my Wonderful Counselor, my Mighty God, my Everlasting Father, and my Prince of Peace. I thank You that Your Kingdom is a government with laws that NEVER change, and that You sent Jesus to guarantee that I have access to justice and can have ALL that You have promised.

I ask for forgiveness for not taking the time to learn how Your Kingdom operates in regard to finances. I grow in confidence as I learn more about Your Kingdom and cast down any earth curse system habits of fear, doubt, or unbelief.

Lord, show me ALL the rights that are legally mine as a citizen of Your Kingdom, and direct me on how to legally claim those rights and release Your promises into my life.

In Jesus's name I pray. Amen.

”

CHAPTER 2

THE BLUE HAZE

ALLEGIANCE [əˈlējəns] – the loyalty of a citizen to his or her government or of a subject to his or her sovereign; commitment and devotion in the firmest sense; faithfulness; obedience

Jesus not only paid for your right to go to heaven, but also He made it possible to live as a son or daughter of God and to enjoy the benefits of the Kingdom of God here in the earth realm.

This short chapter teaches us several important things:

1) The Word works for ________________________.

Write out Acts 10:34:

2) Faith grows by ________________ the Good News of the Kingdom.

Romans 10:17 says, "*Consequently, faith comes from hearing the message, and the message is heard through the* ____________ ______ ___________________________."

Write out John 11:40:

3) God is always faithful to provide everything needed to walk out the direction He gives you.

4) If you are in __________ when you give, the Kingdom connection and flow of the anointing are there.

5) There are millions we are to reach with the Good News of the Gospel, and it takes money to do that.

6) Your life should look different than the rest of the world.

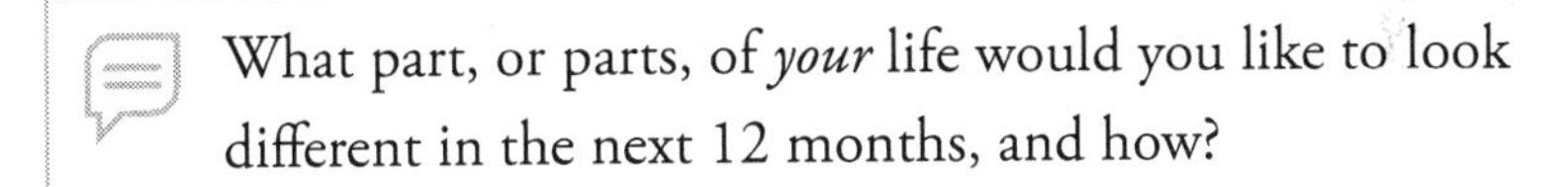

What part, or parts, of *your* life would you like to look different in the next 12 months, and how?

Other notes on this chapter:

Affirming Your Allegiance — Weed Out the Junk

Romans 10:17 tells us that faith comes by *hearing*. Whether you realize it or not, everything you listen to affects you in some way. You may think the sexual song lyrics, the negative news network, the sarcastic talk show host, and the gossiping coworker you've been listening to occasionally are all harmless, but they're not. Whether it's building faith, building fear, or building something else, everything you hear is building something in you. Whatever is going in your ears will ultimately affect your heart, your mind, your attitude, your habits, your character, and your faith.

So, what have you been listening to? This week, really pay attention to what you're hearing each day, and ask God to show you what it's doing to you. Is it helping to build faith or working against it? Write down anything He tells you, and take action. Weed out the junk, and get busy building your faith by feeding on the Word of God.

“

Lord, I thank You that You are always faithful, that You are no respecter of persons, and that You give me favor because I seek Your Kingdom and Your righteousness.

I trust in Your Word that is alive, full of power, and working in me to build faith each and every day.

Lord, show me anything I need to remove from my life that is hindering my faith—anything I've been listening to or hearing that is contrary to Your Word. Give me a craving for Your Word like I've never had before—to read it, to speak it, to act on it, and to live it so that my life looks different than the rest of the world!

In Jesus's name I pray. Amen.

”

CHAPTER 3

PLEASE, GOD, HAVE MERCY!

ALLEGIANCE [əˈlējəns] – the loyalty of a citizen to his or her government or of a subject to his or her sovereign; commitment and devotion in the firmest sense; faithfulness; obedience

You Need Answers

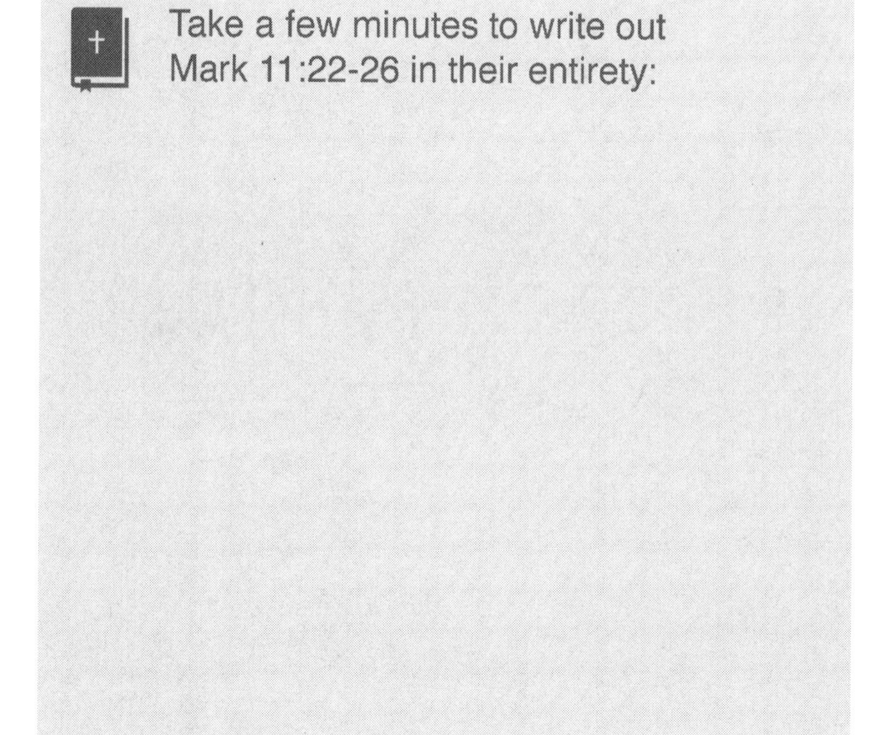

Jerry's story in this chapter shows that no matter how much a person loves God or attends church, they still need to know how to tap into the Kingdom to receive answers.

What other thoughts did you have after reading Jerry's story?

The story of the man whose son was being tormented by evil spirits in Matthew 17:14-20 teach us several things:

1. Begging for mercy when you face a crisis is not your answer. Begging for mercy implies that someone has the power or authority to help but has ___________ not to.

   This is how most people pray. Knowing that God has the power to help but uncertain of His response, they beg for mercy.

2. Giving a long explanation on how the enemy is tormenting you in an attempt to move Jesus to compassion is not your answer. God's heart and desire is to bring freedom. He has no shortage of compassion.

3. The problem with receiving from God is *always* on our end.

   Jesus clearly tells us the reason the demon didn't leave—perverse thinking and unbelief. In other words, wrong thinking and lack of ___________ hindered the Kingdom's jurisdiction in this case.

KNOW THIS: TO GAIN A BASIC UNDERSTANDING OF KINGDOM LAW, YOU MUST UNDERSTAND THAT GOD GAVE ADAM COMPLETE JURISDICTION OVER THE EARTH. HE WAS TO RULE OVER IT.

Jurisdiction

Genesis 1:26 shows us that man was created to rule over the earth. Hebrews 2:7-8 make it very clear:

> *You made him a little lower than the angels; you crowned him with glory and honor and put everything under his feet. In putting everything under him, God left ____________ that is not __________ to him.*

Adam, who had the authority over the earth, cut off God's legal jurisdiction in the earth realm through his rebellion. This means that God, at least for now, can't exercise His authority in the earth realm (the kingdom of men) unless a man or woman who has legal jurisdiction here will come into agreement with Him, which opens the spiritual door for the Kingdom of God to have legal jurisdiction here.

Write out Matthew 18:18:

Jesus is saying here that if a man or a woman will release the Kingdom's ________________ here, the Kingdom will back it up. If we don't, the Kingdom can't.

As a believer, you have spiritual authority in the earth realm. You should be exercising it.

What have you been binding (forbidding) in your life?

What have you been loosing (permitting) in your life?

If a person has no legal remedy to a problem and has no access to a process where justice is served, there is no assurance of answers. _____________ is all that is left to do.

But you don't have to beg. You have access to justice in the Kingdom. There are answers to your problems.

How does the teaching in this chapter on unbelief short-circuiting heaven's jurisdiction change the way you think about things that have happened in your life?

____________ is required for heaven to have jurisdiction in the earth realm.

We see in the story in Matthew 17 that the disciples were not convinced, absolutely __________________, that the demon would come out. They were afraid.

Since man has legality over the earth realm, God's government and His authority can't move until a man or a woman, who has jurisdiction in the earth, is fully persuaded of what heaven says, then releases that authority here.

Faith is being fully persuaded.

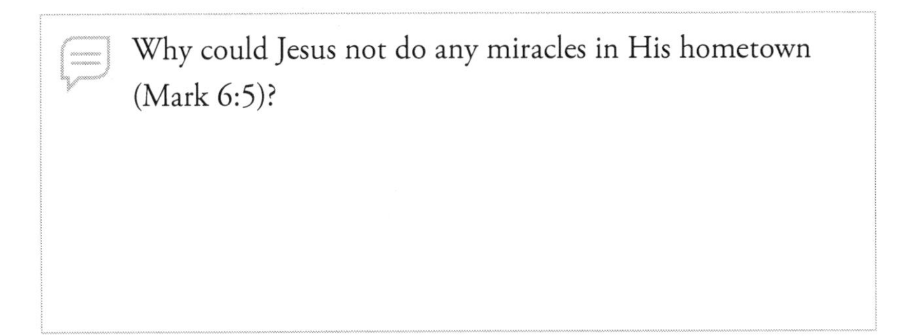
Why could Jesus not do any miracles in His hometown (Mark 6:5)?

KNOW THIS: FAITH (AGREEMENT WITH HEAVEN) GIVES HEAVEN LEGALITY IN THE EARTH REALM.

Write out Romans 10:10:

Justified is a __________ term meaning the administration of law and implies that heaven now has legality in the earth realm.

Two things must take place before heaven's authority and power can be released here in the earth realm:

1. We must be fully persuaded and be in ______________ in our hearts with what heaven says; this is called faith.
2. We need to understand that being in faith by itself will not release heaven here.

How is releasing your Kingdom authority like flipping on a light switch?

What sticks out to you most about the stories of Haley, Joel, and Holland in this chapter?

KNOW THIS: PRAYER DOES NOT RELEASE THE AUTHORITY AND POWER OF GOD. PRAYER GIVES US DIRECTION.

The heart can be fully persuaded of what heaven says, but nothing happens until a man or woman who is in faith releases the _______________ in the earth realm by *speaking* it.

The laws of the Kingdom work every time for anyone who will take the time to learn them and __________ them.

God isn't holding out on you, choosing not to bless you or help you in your time of need. He's already given you the answers.

God has given you _______________ you would ever need in life through Jesus Christ, who through His sacrifice gave you access to ALL that heaven has.

First John 5:14-15 speak of law, and law gives us confidence of obtaining ____________, what is legally ours, because God hears us—He takes the case.

When Christians beg and carry on, it portrays the Kingdom of God as being weak, offering no answers.

What do you realize you've been begging God for that is already legally yours as a citizen of the Kingdom?

Matthew 6:7-13 teach us how to _________.

Confidence in prayer is vital to your life.

Honestly, what adjustments need to be made to your prayer life?

YOUR ANSWER IS TO BELIEVE WHAT GOD SAYS IS YOURS, AND USE YOUR AUTHORITY IN THE KINGDOM OF HEAVEN TO BRING HEAVEN INTO THE EARTH.

How would your prayers be different if you knew without a shadow of a doubt that they would be effective and all of heaven would back them up?

The Kingdom Way of Living

- Knowing exactly what your legal rights are as a citizen of heaven, freely given to you
- Understanding the process to receive, and enjoying the benefit of those laws
- No fear
- No uncertainty, complete confidence in trials
- Nothing but hope for the future
- Free from the "law of sin and death" and access to the "law of the Spirit of life" (Romans 8:2)
- Watching the law of the Spirit of life produce the righteousness of the Kingdom in your life.
- Healing
- Ability to be generous on every occasion

What did you take away from Kirsten's Pomeranian puppy story in this chapter?

Kirsten's Pomeranian puppy showing up was a direct result of the Kingdom and the laws that govern it. The Kingdom produced just like it will __________ time for anyone who has __________ and releases Kingdom ______________ here in the earth realm.

Affirming Your Allegiance — Speak His Word

Take time this week to physically write out this version of 1 John 5:14-15 and post it somewhere where you will see it multiple times per day, like in your car, on your bathroom mirror, on your desk, or as your phone screen saver. Read these two verses aloud each time you see them.

> **This is the confidence I have in approaching God: that if I ask ANYTHING according to His will, He HEARS ME. And if I KNOW that He hears me—whatever I ask—I KNOW that I HAVE what I asked of Him.**

“

Lord, thank You for uncovering more and more about how Your Kingdom operates through Your Word as I read it and go through this study.

Help me to recognize and overcome anything I've ever believed that was wrong about Your character.

I praise You for teaching me how to pray and to speak Kingdom authority in the earth realm. I am confident that if I ask anything according to Your will, You hear me—You take the case on my behalf. And I know that I have what I ask.

In Jesus's name I pray. Amen.

”

CHAPTER 4

THE GIANT FISH

ALLEGIANCE [əˈlējəns] – the loyalty of a citizen to his or her government or of a subject to his or her sovereign; commitment and devotion in the firmest sense; faithfulness; obedience

It's Your Choice

You are the one who is determining how you live.

The Kingdom of God can impact every area of your life, but you're the one who has to release the _______________ that you need or want into your life. It won't just happen by itself.

This short chapter teaches us several important things:

1. Nothing is too small or unimportant to bring under the _____________ of the Kingdom.

Write out Luke 12:6-7:

Jesus commands you not to worry in Matthew 6:25-33.

What have you found yourself worrying about? Write it down here:

Read this adapted prayer from Matthew 6:25-33 aloud, inserting anything you wrote down that you've been worrying about:

I will not worry about: ________________________________

________________________.

Jesus told me to look at the birds. They don't sow, reap, or store away in barns, and God takes excellent care of them. They don't sit around worrying. And Jesus said I am much more valuable to Him than the birds are.

There is no point in worrying. It adds nothing to my life.

God knows exactly what I need when I need it. I will seek His Kingdom FIRST, above all else, and His righteousness; and He will give me everything I need for: ________________________

________________________.

2. Don't quit, no matter how hard it seems or how hard something might be trying to pull you down.

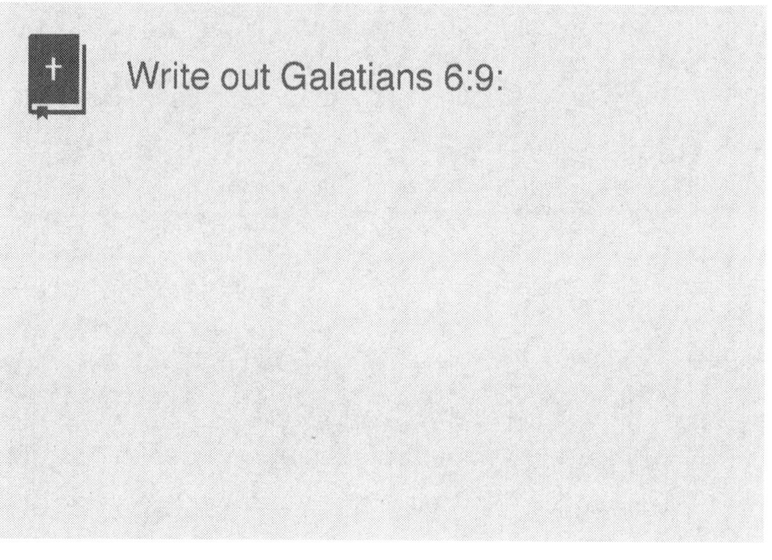

Describe a time when you didn't give up and the results:

3. God is faithful.

What are five things in your life that you think are too small or unimportant for God to care about?

1. ______________________________
____

2. ______________________________
____

3. ______________________________
____

4. ______________________________
____

5. ______________________________
____

Other notes about this chapter:

Affirming Your Allegiance — Give Him All of It

The New Living Translation of Psalm 37:23 says, "*The Lord directs the steps of the godly. He delights in every detail of their lives.*"

See that? He delights in every *detail* of your life.

God isn't a sometime God—He doesn't want you to come to Him for the "big" things and then go off and try to take care of the "little" things by yourself. He cares about every detail of your life, and He wants to be involved.

So, this week, take the list of five things you wrote down in this chapter—those five *details* of your life you saw as too small or unimportant for God to concern Himself with—and pray over each one, acknowledging that He cares about every *detail* of your life and placing even those "small" things under the dominion of His Kingdom. Remind yourself daily, if you have to, that God cares just as much about the little things, until you get in the habit of giving everything to Him.

Expect answers, and be sure to record what happens. As you look back over all of the "little" things God has done, it will help build your faith for the big things.

“

Lord, I praise You for loving me. You know me far better than I know myself, and you care about every detail, down to the number of hairs on my head.

I will approach You confidently from this point on with the things I think are small or unimportant, as well as the big things, because I know Your will for me is ALWAYS good, and You are ALWAYS faithful.

Help me to not leave anything in my life, big or small, under the jurisdiction of the world's system but to bring every aspect of my life under the jurisdiction of Your Kingdom, so I can live in victory.

In Jesus's name I pray. Amen.

”

CHAPTER 5

WHOSE CHOICE WAS IT?

ALLEGIANCE [ə'lējəns] – the loyalty of a citizen to his or her government or of a subject to his or her sovereign; commitment and devotion in the firmest sense; faithfulness; obedience

Again, It's Your Choice

Second Peter 1:3a tells you that God's divine power has given you ____________________ you need for life and godliness.

Again, notice that is *past tense*. God has *already* provided everything you need for life and godliness. Every one of His promises is available to you.

The story of the woman with the issue of blood in Luke 8:42-48 teaches us several things:

1. It was her ____________ to be healed that day.

   Jesus didn't even know she was there.

   So many people think they're "waiting" for God to do something in their lives. But God doesn't randomly choose to heal one person one day and not someone else. He's already given _____ of us access to healing through our legal standing in His Kingdom.

2. Her _________ allowed her to tap into the power of the Kingdom and receive her healing.

What Is Faith?

Your understanding of this most basic law of the Kingdom is life or death.

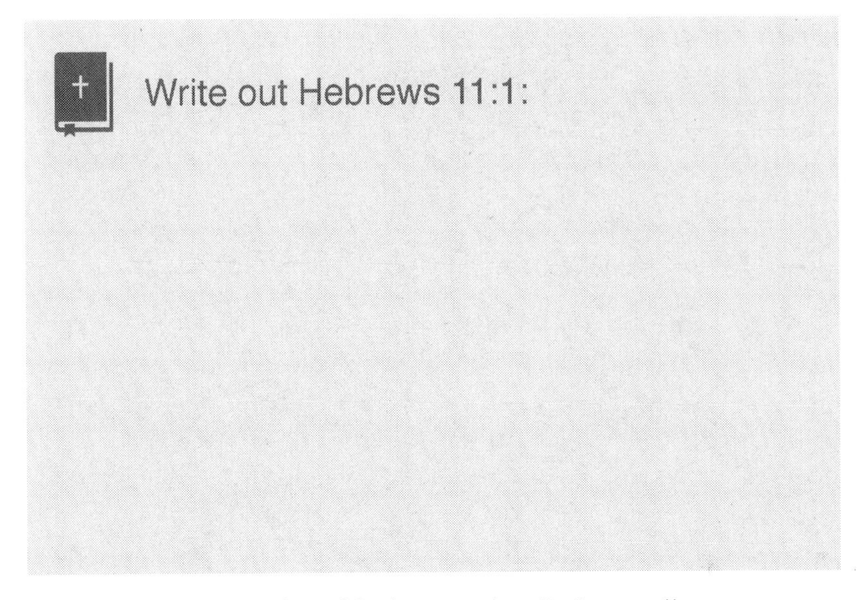

This tells us the benefits of faith, not what faith actually is.

Look at Romans 4:18-21:

> *Against all hope, Abraham in hope believed and so became the father of many nations, just as it had been said to him, "So shall your offspring be." Without weakening in his faith, he faced the fact that his body was as good as dead—since he was about a hundred years old—and that Sarah's womb was also dead. Yet he did not waver through unbelief regarding the ______________ of God, but was strengthened in his faith and gave glory to God, ____________ ______________ ______________________that God had power to do what he had promised.*

So faith is being fully persuaded that God has the power to do what He has promised.

Faith is being in ________________ with heaven, not just mentally but fully persuaded, your heart settled and ________________ totally of what God has said, in spite of the natural realm indicating something else.

How does this change how you've always defined faith in your own life?

Why Is Faith Needed?

What did you learn from this chapter about delegated authority?

KNOW THIS: MAN IS STILL THE LEGAL RULER OVER THE EARTH REALM, BUT HE HAS NO AUTHORITY. THIS IS WHY GOD HAS TO USE SPIRIT-FILLED PEOPLE TO BRING ABOUT HIS WILL IN THE LIVES OF MEN.

The principle of man's _______________ over the earth is vital to your understanding of Kingdom law.

How does the example about a leased property and a landlord used in this chapter help clarify for you why God can't just burst into the affairs of men?

_______________ is called the father of our faith because he is the man that opened the door of the earth realm to God whereby all nations on the earth would be blessed.

Abraham's _________ opened a legal doorway for heaven, which God locked permanently open by making a legal agreement (_____________) with Abraham and his seed, or heirs.

KNOW THIS: HEAVEN CAN ONLY LEGALLY AFFECT A MAN OR WOMAN IN THE EARTH REALM WHO DESIRES AND CHOOSES TO COME UNDER GOD'S DOMINION AND AUTHORITY.

Although Abraham's heirs had the legal agreement available to them, they each still had to fulfill the legal requirement of their own __________, being fully persuaded of what God said, to actually enjoy the personal benefits of the agreement that God and Abraham had made.

How Do You *Get* Faith?

Mark 4 tells us in three parables.

The Parable of the Man Scattering Seed

The seed is the ________ of God, and the ground is the _________ of man or the spirit of man.

Jesus is saying a man scatters the Word of God into his _________ heart. Then all ____ ___________ the soil, or the heart, of man starts to produce faith (agreement with heaven) in the earth realm.

KNOW THIS: AS YOU KEEP THE WORD IN YOUR HEART, YOUR HEART SLOWLY COMES INTO AGREEMENT WITH WHAT HEAVEN SAYS, AND FAITH IS PRODUCED.

Describe how the process of building faith is like a plant growing from a sprout to full maturity:

In the natural realm, when the seed in the head is mature, it will look __________ like the seed that was sown into the ground.

When that Word matures in your heart, the confidence that you have in the promise becomes what you believe and say. You're no longer simply quoting what heaven says. Your heart is firmly convinced.

There is a ________________ ____________________ of what heaven says when faith is there.

KNOW THIS: YOUR WORDS AND ACTIONS ARE THE SWITCHES THAT RELEASE HEAVEN'S POWER INTO THE EARTH REALM.

Write out Mark 4:28:

Faith isn't a product of heaven; it's a product of your ____________.

What is the only way you can get faith?

When the harvest of your faith is available, what must you do?

What is the "sickle"? ____________ _______________

Write out Proverbs 18:21:

Mastering the formula of saying the right thing isn't the key by itself, as Mark 11:23 shows us:

I tell you the truth, if anyone _______ to this mountain, "Go, throw yourself into the sea," and does not doubt in his heart but _____________ that what ____ ________ will happen, it will be done for him.

The test of faith is if _______ believe what you are saying.

Read Luke 6:45 and Proverbs 4:23-24 and think about what has been coming out of your mouth recently.

What are some words you know you need to eliminate from your vocabulary?

How Do You Know if You're Actually in Faith?

In Faith	Not in Faith
• Mental agreement	• Doubt
• Peace and joy	• Fear-based decisions
• Confident expectation	• Worry
• Knowing despite circumstances	• Double-minded
• Able to defend your position spiritually, stand on a promise, anchored in Scripture	• Unable to defend your position spiritually, unable to give Scripture
• Confidence in the Word of God	• Confidence in own actions or formula
• Know and agree with the will of God for the situation	• Unsure of or incorrect about the will of God for the situation

Describe a time in your life when you knew your only hope was the Word of God:

What is one situation in your life you know you need to properly develop faith for after reading this chapter?

Are you prone to letting go of the Word when you're under pressure? If so, what are you going to do about it?

Affirming Your Allegiance — Bind and Loose

"The tongue has the power of life and death, and those who love it will eat its fruit" (Proverbs 18:21).

You can't overestimate the power of your words. Your words are what heaven binds or looses. You have the keys of the Kingdom here in the earth realm. There's a lot of responsibility in having that authority.

Many Christians seem to think that God stops all of heaven to listen when they pray, but the reality is that they're speaking—binding and loosing—all the time, with every word, not just when they pray.

The Bible tells us in Matthew 12:36 that we'll have to give an account for every careless word we've spoken. Why? Because God has seated us with Christ in heavenly places. We are ruling on behalf of the King and will be held accountable for what we've decreed.

Don't fear that authority; rejoice in it.

This week, really pay attention to what's coming out of your mouth. Speak life wherever you go. Decree provision, healing, direction, wisdom, favor, and health—all of the promises God has given you. Use your words wisely.

Lord, I receive Your help, by faith, with putting a watch over my mouth. Help me to control my tongue, Father, and speak only excellent things that bring glory to Your name. Your Word teaches me that the power of life and death are in my mouth, so I refrain from using words or taking part in conversations that are useless, pointless, foolish, wicked, or corrupt. I am slow to speak and choose to speak life when I do speak.

In Jesus's name I pray. Amen.

CHAPTER 6

THE BLESSING OF THE LORD

ALLEGIANCE [əˈlējəns] – the loyalty of a citizen to his or her government or of a subject to his or her sovereign; commitment and devotion in the firmest sense; faithfulness; obedience

The Kingdom Works Every Time

What keys about the Kingdom of God and faith can you take from the stories shared at the beginning of this chapter?

- God created man and put everything under his _______________.

- Man ruled the earth from a position of _______________ _______________ and wore the crown of the government he represented—God's Kingdom.

- Satan, who had already been cast to earth, hated man and lusted after the authority he possessed.

- Adam and Eve lost their legal position of authority in God's Kingdom when they chose to believe Satan and disobey God. They essentially kicked God out.

- This decision had tremendous ramifications on the earth and on every man and woman who would ever live.

    ? Adam's own ____________ ________ and __________ would be required for the earth to produce what he needed for survival. I call this the ____________________________________.

    ? David calls it the ______________________________ ____________ in Psalm 23:4.

God's Kingdom System

- Life
- Identity in God-given assignment and purpose
- Peace
- Excitement to get to work on strategies and ideas from God
- Joy
- Energized by seeing the Kingdom of God operate
- Hope

Earth Curse System

- Survival, consumed with finding or hoarding wealth
- Identity in money, possessions, power, and performance
- Fear
- Goal is to stop… Looking for a way out… Dread Mondays… Only look forward to weekends, vacations, or retirement
- Dysfunction
- Exhaustion
- Little to no hope for a better future

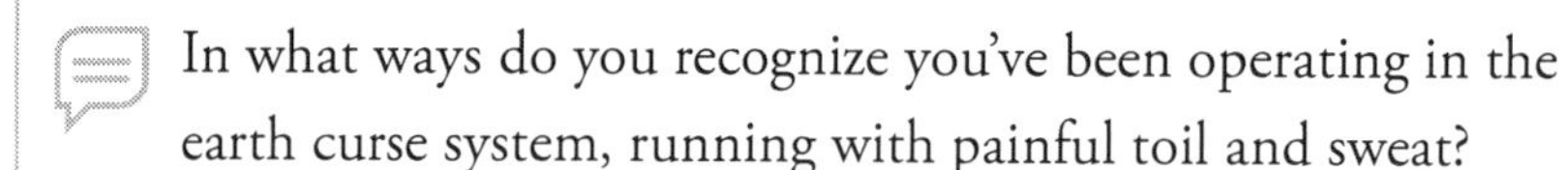

In what ways do you recognize you've been operating in the earth curse system, running with painful toil and sweat?

Running with painful toil and sweat is the only system we know, but everyone dreams of _________.

In an average day, how many hours do you think about money, either acquiring it or protecting what you have? _______________

You were created to be active in your assignment, your uniquely created purpose.

What dreams have you put on hold or given up on because you've been too busy running just to survive?

You will never discover your created purpose until you __________ _____ __________ ________.

What's one thing you're really passionate about?

What would happen if you were able to focus on that passion?

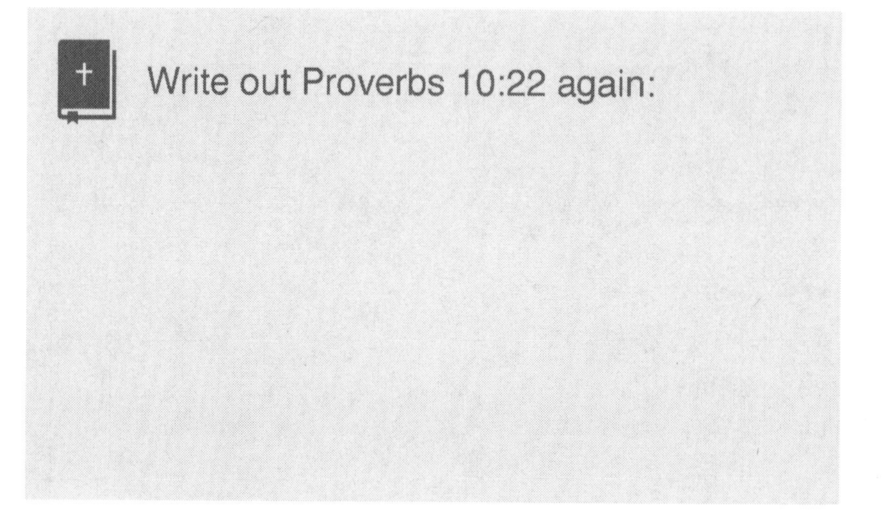

KNOW THIS: THE KINGDOM OF GOD PROVIDES A WAY OF ESCAPE FROM THE PAINFUL TOIL AND SWEAT SYSTEM THAT ADAM LEFT US WITH.

Provision is ______________________.

Without provision there can be no vision, because being without it makes obtaining it your vision. This is slavery in its most deceptive form.

Affirming Your Allegiance — Dream the Impossible

Jeremiah 29:11 tells you that God has great plans for you, plans to prosper you and to give you hope and a future. God has big dreams for you, and He wants to reveal them to you.

Take time this week to *dream*. Every day, take a few minutes to dream. Dream about something that gets you out of bed in the morning, motivates you, and pulls on you. Dream about what you would be doing if you were following your passions, using your talents, making a difference in the world, and winning in life.

And write them down. Even if you have no clue how they could possibly happen; or you see no ability in yourself for them come to pass; or you've already tried over and over again in your own strength, write them down.

Because God-sized dreams are always too big for you to do on your own.

As you believe His Word, His Kingdom principles, and His promises, you WILL see the incredible and enjoy the impossible in your life. And you're going to want a record of it.

“

Lord, I thank You that You are able to do exceedingly abundantly above and beyond all that I can ever ask, hope, think, or dream according to Your great power that is at work in me!

Father, Your Word tells me that You know the plans You have for me—plans to prosper me and not harm me, and to give me a hope and a future. I thank You that You don't just see me as I am right now, but You see all I can become.

I thank You that I am a believer and not a doubter, that You give me Your dreams for my life, and that I walk by faith.

Help me to "fix my money thing" and discover the talents You have placed in me, so I can walk in the great purpose You have for my life.

In Jesus's name I pray. Amen.

”

CHAPTER 7

THE DOOR

ALLEGIANCE [əˈlējəns] – the loyalty of a citizen to his or her government or of a subject to his or her sovereign; commitment and devotion in the firmest sense; faithfulness; obedience

God Wants You to Prosper

Hell was never created for man or with man in mind. It was never God's intention that any man go to hell.

> *Then he will say to those on his left, "Depart from me, you who are cursed, into the eternal fire prepared for ______________ ______________________."*
>
> —Matthew 25:41

To rescue man from this fate, God had to reestablish His government's _________________ in the earth.

What was the only way this could happen?

For God's plan to work and to prove the ______________ of that plan in the earth realm to Satan, who would surely cry foul, God would need to find a man and woman who would believe Him for a child when it was totally and permanently impossible for them to ever have a child.

They would have to believe God to do the ______________.

This would give God the legality He needed to later place His seed in Mary, Jesus's mother.

Why MUST the lineage of Jesus be recorded at the beginning of Matthew?

What major change did God's covenant with Abraham bring in regard to provision?

KNOW THIS: AS LONG AS ABRAHAM'S HEIRS STAYED TRUE TO THEIR COVENANT AND WORSHIPED GOD, HE MADE THEM PROSPEROUS.

God is NOT a hard taskmaster. He wants to ______________ your finances.

God Wants to Establish You

The Lord will send a blessing on your barns and on ____________________ you put your hand to. The Lord your God will bless you __________________ he is giving you. The Lord will ____________________ you as his holy people, as he promised you on oath, if you ________________________ of the Lord your God and walk in his ways. Then all the peoples on earth will see that you are called by the name of the Lord, and they will fear you. The Lord will ____________________ ____—in the fruit of your womb, the young of your livestock and the crops of your ground—in the land he swore to your forefathers to give you.

The Lord will ______________________________, the storehouse of his bounty, to send rain on your land in season and to bless ___ the work of your hands. You will _______ to many nations but will borrow from none. The Lord will make you the ________, not the tail. If you ________________________ to the commands of the Lord your God that I give you this day and carefully ____________ them, you will always be at the _______, never at the bottom.

Describe what "financially established" would look like for you:

Affirming Your Allegiance — Believe and Trust

I love how 2 Chronicles 20:20b reads in the Amplified Bible:

> *"Believe* and *trust in the Lord your God and you will be established (secure). Believe* and *trust in His prophets and succeed."*

Here's the thing: I can tell you to believe and trust in God all I want, but before you can, you need to know what you really believe about Him and about His character.

See, so many people have been tricked into believing that God isn't good. Satan has worked overtime for more than 2,000 years telling people lies and distorting the character of God. It's his goal to convince as many people as possible that God isn't good or trustworthy.

Satan wants you to believe that God is unpredictable; that He's good to some people, but that He "allows" bad things to happen to teach people a lesson; that He doesn't heal everyone; that He takes people from earth early because He "needs another angel in heaven"; or that He just flat out expects too much.

But those are lies. That's not God's character.

To say that God does bad things to good people doesn't match what the Bible says about Him and who He is.

God is faithful, and His Kingdom works every time.

It's vital that you have complete confidence in God's character and His Word, or you can never believe and trust in Him to establish (secure) you.

Take time this week to really study and meditate on the character of God. Here are some Scriptures to help you get started:

Hebrews 13:8
Ephesians 2:4-5
James 1:17
2 Peter 3:9
1 John 4:8
1 John 1:5
Isaiah 40:28
Ephesians 2:8-9
Isaiah 41:10
John 3:17

"

Lord, because You are faithful and trustworthy, I commit to trust You with all my heart and lean not on my own understanding. In all my ways, I will acknowledge You, and You will make my paths straight.

I listen diligently to Your voice and follow Your commandments. You are my confidence. Because I believe in and trust in You, You establish and secure me. I walk in Your continued favor and blessings.

Thank You, Father, that You have made me the head and not the tail, that I am above only and not beneath anyone or anything.

In Jesus's name I pray. Amen.

"

CHAPTER 8

THE POWER OF ALLEGIANCE

ALLEGIANCE [ə'lējəns] – the loyalty of a citizen to his or her government or of a subject to his or her sovereign; commitment and devotion in the firmest sense; faithfulness; obedience

The Most Powerful Principle

What does Genesis 39:2a, "*The Lord was with Joseph and he prospered*" mean? Isn't the Lord with everyone?

KNOW THIS: GOD DOESN'T HAVE THE LEGALITY OR JURISDICTION IN THE EARTH REALM WITHOUT A LEGAL AGREEMENT—A COVENANT IN PLACE—WITH A MAN OR WOMAN ON THE EARTH.

Ephesians 2:12 tells us that without a ________________ people are without hope and without God in the world.

"God was with Joseph" meant that God had legal influence in Joseph's life through the covenant that Joseph's grandfather Abraham had put in place.

This legal covenant, allowing God's ______________ and ________________, overrode the earth realm's painful toil and sweat system. It was legal for God to bless Joseph.

When you prosper with God's help, the people who are living under the earth curse system of survival notice the difference.

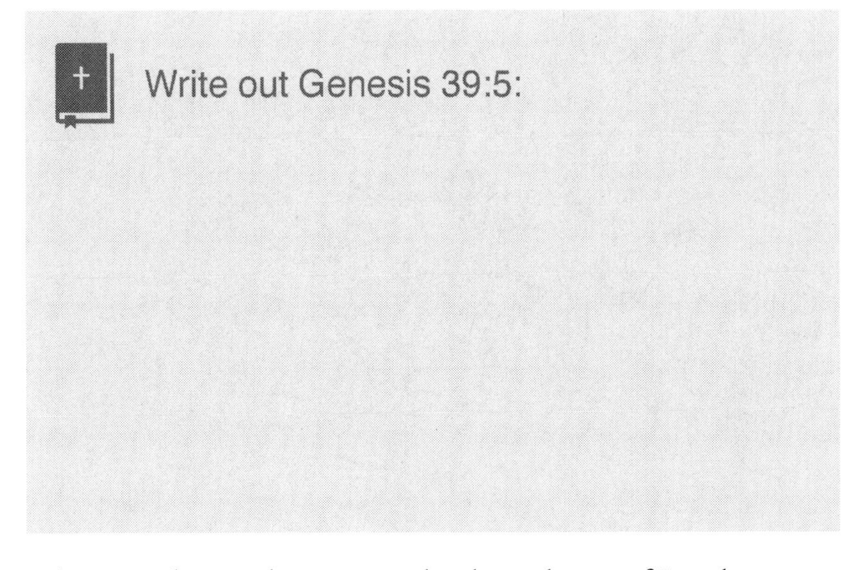

When Potiphar put his estate under the authority of Joseph, without knowing it, his estate came under the covenant that Joseph had with God.

Potiphar's stuff—his estate—and property ____________________
_________________________.

When Potiphar placed his estate under the ____________________ of Joseph's authority, he was also placing it under the influence of the blessing of God.

The Sabbath Rest

The ________________________ day was a picture of the day when man would no longer have to strive with his own painful toil and sweat just to survive.

The Sabbath was only made possible by the ________________
__________________.

The double portion is simply having _____ __ _______
_________________________, or having something *abundantly* supplied.

The Sabbath rest is still available to you today.

How would having more than enough change your life right now?

Potiphar brought his problems and worries under the jurisdiction of the Kingdom of God, aligning himself with God, and changing __________________.

That was his answer.

It's your answer too.

Affirming Your Allegiance — Check Your Attitude

His family was dysfunctional. His brothers hated him. They sold him into slavery and pretended a wild animal had killed him. When things finally seemed to be getting better, he ended up wrongly accused and in prison.

Reading all of that, you wouldn't be surprised if the guy we were talking about had a serious attitude problem, right?

> Attitude – *a settled way of thinking or feeling about someone or something, typically one that is reflected in a person's behavior.*

But, of course, this is the story of Joseph. And nowhere in the Bible do we read that Joseph had an attitude problem. He wasn't angry, set on revenge, having pity parties (because he really could've had quite a few), or blaming anyone else for what had happened to him. In fact, in every bad situation Joseph faced, he still maintained a good attitude—an attitude of *faith*.

Joseph wasn't special. He didn't get an extra dose of patience or a bigger dose of faith than any of the rest of us. He was just a guy walking it out like all of the rest of us.

Check your attitude this week. Is your "settled way of thinking or feeling that is reflected in your behavior" one of faith?

If not, it's time to make some changes.

Keeping your attitude in check starts with keeping your thoughts in check. The Bible says you're to take every thought captive to make it obedient to Christ. Plain and simple, your brain doesn't have the authority to think whatever it wants. No matter what's happening around you, you can *choose* what you think about.

So, pay attention to what you're thinking. Renew your mind with the Word of God, and speak what God says. Be determined to keep an attitude of faith, despite your circumstances, and watch what God does.

> *Father, I thank You for clearly revealing the power of allegiance to Your Kingdom. I praise You that You are with me as You were with Joseph and that You give me success in everything I do!*
>
> *I take captive every thought to make it obedient to Christ. I am transformed by the renewing of my mind to Your Word. I fix my thoughts on what is true, noble, right, pure, lovely, admirable, excellent, and praiseworthy; and I am a new creation in Christ Jesus.*
>
> *In Jesus's name I pray. Amen.*

CHAPTER 9

YOU FEED THEM!

ALLEGIANCE [əˈlējəns] – the loyalty of a citizen to his or her government or of a subject to his or her sovereign; commitment and devotion in the firmest sense; faithfulness; obedience

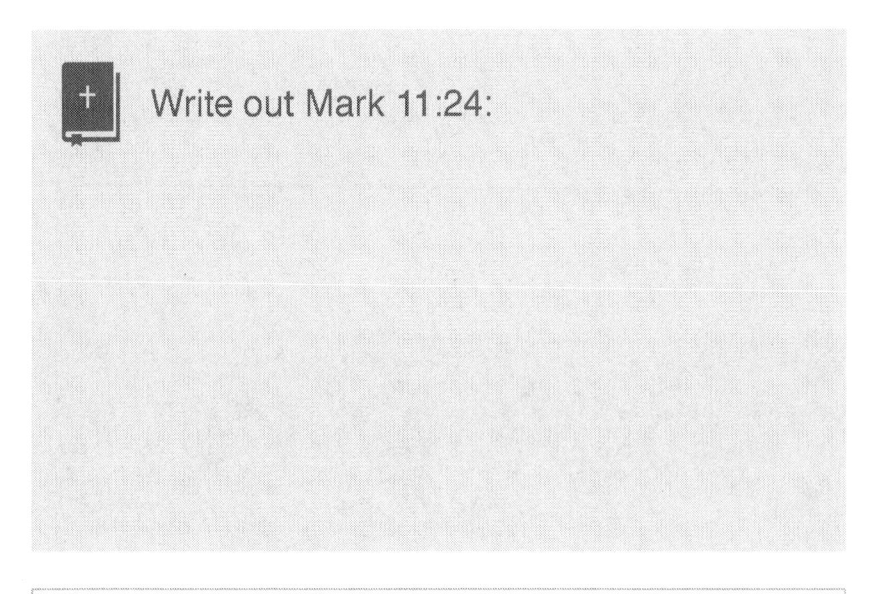

What insight concerning the Kingdom and how it functions can you take from Don's blue marlin story shared in this chapter?

KNOW THIS: JUST LIKE THE WIND CAN'T BE SEEN BUT HAS A VISIBLE EFFECT ON THE NATURAL REALM, SO THE KINGDOM OF GOD IS REAL AND HAS AN EFFECT IN THE NATURAL REALM.

When Jesus told the disciples to feed the crowd, they reacted with the typical mind-set of the earth curse system, immediately converting their lack of provision to the earth curse system of economics and painful toil and sweat—eight months of it to be exact.

In what ways do you realize that you've been filtering your future through the earth curse system of thinking?

If you filter every idea through the ______________________________ ____________, you will never tap into the Kingdom way of living, because God is not tied to that system.

If you want to engage the Kingdom, you have to start thinking Kingdom thoughts—________ things are possible!

When you don't have provision, your ____________ dies.

What steps did Jesus take that you need to follow?

1. **Sow a portion of ____________________________________.**
   This is the first step in operating by Kingdom laws. Jesus identified something that they currently had that could be put under the government of God. Once that asset was transferred to God's domain, He would then have legal access to multiply or affect change with it.

_____________ is a barter system. You and I "name" money every day. Money becomes whatever we need.

2. **Put it under the** ______________________________.
To do this, you simply do what Jesus did. You lay your hands on your gift, and you speak over it. You pray, and release it into the Kingdom of God with your words. Remember, God created everything with words, and you have the power of the Kingdom backing your words.

How does the story of Peter letting Jesus use his fishing boat illustrate the power of allegiance?

How does the story of Chris and the cheesecake idea in this chapter inspire you?

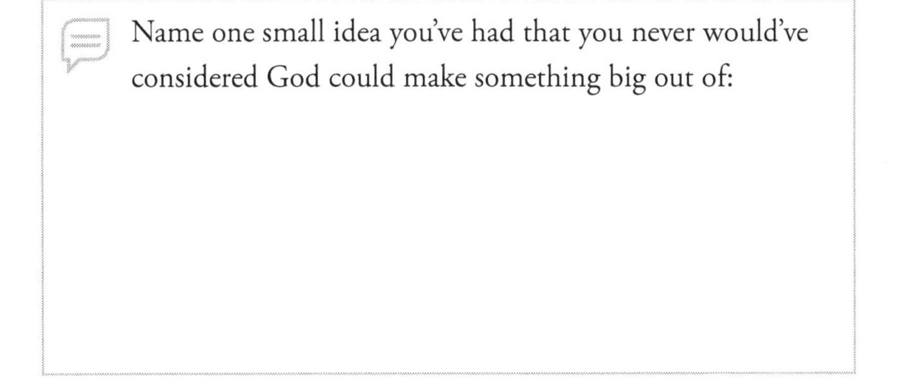

Name one small idea you've had that you never would've considered God could make something big out of:

Affirming Your Allegiance — Where Your Money Is

Matthew 6:21 says, *"For where your treasure is, there your heart will be also."*

Show me your bank account statement, and I'll tell you what you love.

Does your money show your allegiance to the Kingdom of God or to something else?

Money is meant to be a tool of influence for the Kingdom of God. It's important to God, and He wants you to have it. But money shouldn't have you. And neither should the things that money can buy.

God wants you to have His heart, and to be able to be generous on every occasion (2 Corinthians 9:8-11), to meet the needs of people so they will see Him through you. Paul tells us in Second Corinthians 9:13 that as you help people with your money, those people will praise God because they see that you cared for them in the name of the Lord.

Giving is also the doorway that gives God the opportunity to bless you with opportunities, direction, concepts, and ideas that will propel your life financially. God wants you blessed and prosperous.

This week, ask yourself these important questions:

> What does the way you spend your money say about the desires of your heart?
>
> Are you trusting in the world's system of debt over God's system?
>
> What does your money say about your allegiance?

Take time to study Luke 16:11-13 and pray about your finances.

"

Lord, I ask for forgiveness for trusting in the world's system of debt over Your system. From this day forward, my money will reflect my allegiance to Your Kingdom.

I want to live so that people see You through me, especially with my finances. Help me to be generous on every occasion, meeting the needs of people in Your Name.

Because I am trustworthy with worldly wealth, You trust me with true riches, and give to me good measure, pressed down, shaken together, and running over!

In Jesus's name I pray. Amen.

"

CHAPTER 10

GATHER, NOT LATHER!

ALLEGIANCE [ə'lējəns] – the loyalty of a citizen to his or her government or of a subject to his or her sovereign; commitment and devotion in the firmest sense; faithfulness; obedience

Have you ever seen a horse in the summer after a long run? They're covered in a foamy kind of sweat called lather. That's one way you can tell they've been working hard.

It's About *How* You Work

By having what you need in life, you are able to labor in the ______________, being about your Father's business and your __________________.

In Matthew 17, Peter asked Jesus about paying their taxes.

In verse 27, Jesus simply told Peter where the _________________ was, the _____________ he needed to use to harvest it, and exactly what he should be looking for. All Peter had to do was go _______________ it.

Look at Matthew 6:24-34 again. What are three things that stand out to you the most from these Scriptures?

1. ____
2. ____
3. ____

God wants to be __________ in your life.

If ____________ is your treasure, it will be first, demanding your time, your priorities, and your affection.

This is why God has to train you to ____________.

KNOW THIS: IF GOD DIDN'T WANT YOU TO HAVE THINGS, JESUS WOULD'VE SAID SO. INSTEAD, HE SAYS THAT ALL OF THESE THINGS THE WORLD RUNS AFTER SHALL BE ADDED TO YOUR LIFE IF YOU LIVE GOD'S WAY.

What does "seek the Kingdom of God" mean?

Affirming Your Allegiance — Walk Out His Vision

It's time to throw off the old government of the earth curse system, with all of its lack and despair, and enjoy a new way of living—living in the Kingdom of God, with new laws, no lack, and great joy!

It's time to get a new vision for your life, to look at the future with excitement!

How can you walk out God's vision for your life? Start here:

1. Shut out distractions, get alone with God, and listen for His direction.

2. Write down what He reveals to you. (Habakkuk 2:2 tells us to write the vision and make it plain.)

3. Post it where you can read it at least once a day. Create a vision board with words and images.

4. Move forward in faith, believing God for opportunities and provision.

"

Lord, I thank You that You have already given me everything I need for life and godliness and that I receive everything I need through knowing You and reading Your Word.

Father, You are my treasure! You are in first place in my life. I don't run after the things of the world, but all the things the world runs after are added to my life because I seek You FIRST.

Thank you for the incredible vision You have for my life and for training me to gather on assignment! I labor only in the Kingdom, being about Your business and my God-designed purpose.

In Jesus's name I pray. Amen.

"

CHAPTER 11

FLYING IS EASIER THAN WALKING

ALLEGIANCE [əˈlējəns] – the loyalty of a citizen to his or her government or of a subject to his or her sovereign; commitment and devotion in the firmest sense; faithfulness; obedience

Leave Your Slow Methods Behind

Just like the law of gravity or the laws of flight, the laws of the Kingdom do not change.

You limit yourself by weighing your future against what you think is possible.

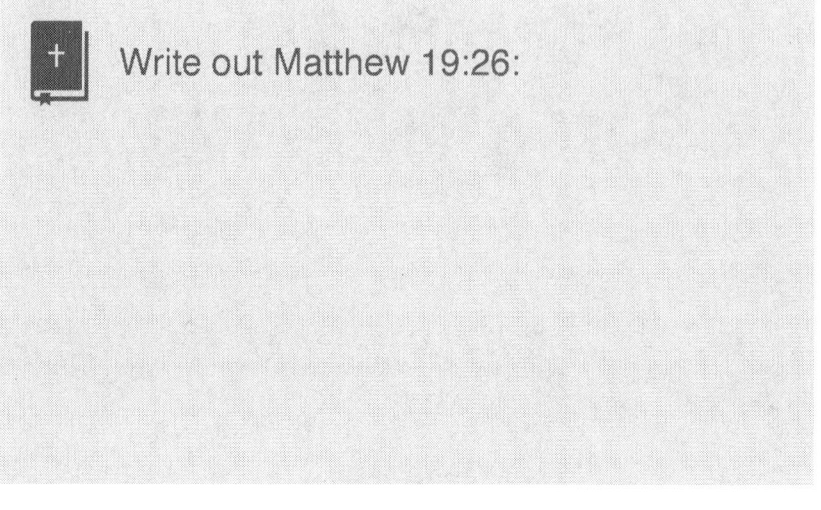

With God, all things are possible if you'll allow God's ________ to change your ________________.

Do not conform to the pattern of this world, but be ____________________ by the _______________________ of your mind. Then you will be able to test and approve what God's will is—his good, pleasing and perfect will.

—Romans 12:2

Paul is referring to the __________ __________ __________________ and how you think.

What have you been doing in your life using the same "pattern" or "blueprint" every time, but expecting different results?

KNOW THIS: YOUR LIFE DOESN'T HAVE TO BE CONFINED TO SURVIVAL AND FEAR. YOUR LIFE CAN BE TRANSFORMED TO A LIFE OF UNLIMITED POSSIBILITIES WHEN YOU TAP INTO THE LAWS OF THE KINGDOM OF GOD.

What keys about the Kingdom can you take away from the stories in this chapter?

Write out Matthew 11:28:

Jesus came to take your yoke, the _________ _____ ____ _____________, required by the earth curse system, from you.

You can take His yoke (it is already finished) and find ___________ (the seventh day, the true Sabbath) for your soul.

Affirming Your Allegiance — Declare It

Fill *your name* in the blanks in these declarations and say them aloud.

- I, ____________________________________, make a decision today to align myself with God's Kingdom laws and to begin to enjoy the power of allegiance immediately.

- I, ____________________________________, begin my financial revolution today, throwing off the old way of living, the old government, the earth curse system of poverty, sickness, and hopelessness.

I, ______________________________, leave all of my old "caterpillar" ways behind and will FLY by tapping into all of the rights and benefits Jesus gave me access to as a coheir with Him of the Kingdom.

> *Lord, I praise You that You are good and Your Kingdom is good. Thank You that You give me rest when I am weary and burdened. I trade my yoke of painful toil and sweat required by the earth curse system for Your yoke that is easy and light, and find rest for my soul as I learn from You.*
>
> *In Jesus's name I pray. Amen.*

ANSWER KEY

Chapter One

Unresolved financial issues and financial stress make living with fear a way of life.

Good news to a poor man is that he can be free.

As a believer, you can love God, go to church, tithe, and be on your way to heaven, but you MUST learn how to bring the power and authority of the Kingdom into your life to affect your natural circumstances.

The authority of the King flows down through the Kingdom with delegated authority through various government offices and people who operate under that authority.

A kingdom is a group of people who are held together by law or government.

Isaiah 9:6-7 say,

> *For to us a child is born, to us a son is given, and the government will be on his shoulders. And he will be called Wonderful Counselor, Mighty God, Everlasting Father, Prince of Peace.*
>
> *Of the increase of his government and peace there will be no end. He will reign on David's throne and over His Kingdom, establishing and upholding it with justice and righteousness from that time on and forever. The zeal of the Lord Almighty will accomplish this.*

Jesus is the head of this government.

Ephesians 2:19 says you are not only a citizen of the Kingdom of God, but also a member of His very own household, a son or daughter of the King.

God's Kingdom is established and upheld through justice, the administration of God's law.

To ensure that you have what God says is right within His Kingdom, what is legally yours as a citizen in that Kingdom, God has given you access to justice—the process or guarantee that you will have what He has promised you.

Second Corinthians 2:20 clearly says that every promise is "Yes" and "Amen." It has already been decided; it is legally yours.

If you know the law of God's Kingdom (His will), and you know that you have access to justice—the process of enforcement that guarantees you what the law says—then you can be confident and not afraid.

First John 5:14-15 say, "*This is the confidence we have in approaching God: that if we ask anything according to his will, he hears us.*"

This tells you that your answer for your finances is His Kingdom—knowing how to tap into the laws of the Kingdom here in the earth realm, just as Jesus did, is your answer.

If you don't understand spiritual laws, you won't have the ability to enjoy their benefit or to duplicate them when you need them.

Chapter Two

1. The Word works for anyone.

2. Faith grows by hearing the Good News of the Kingdom.

   Romans 10:17 says, "*Consequently, faith comes from hearing the message, and the message is heard through the word of Christ.*"

4. If you are in faith when you give, the Kingdom connection and flow of the anointing are there.

Chapter Three

1. Begging for mercy when you face a crisis is not your answer. Begging for mercy implies that someone has the power or authority to help but has chosen not to.

3. The problem with receiving from God is always on our end.

   Jesus clearly tells us the reason the demon didn't leave—perverse thinking and unbelief. In other words, wrong thinking and lack of faith hindered the Kingdom's jurisdiction in this case.

You made him a little lower than the angels; you crowned him with glory and honor and put everything under his feet. In putting everything under him, God left nothing that is not subject to him.

Jesus is saying here that if a man or a woman will release heaven's (the Kingdom's) authority here, heaven (the Kingdom) will back it up. If we don't, heaven (the Kingdom) can't.

If a person has no legal remedy to a problem and has no access to a process where justice is served, there is no assurance of answers. Begging is all that is left to do.

Faith is required for heaven to have jurisdiction in the earth realm.

We see in the story in Matthew 17 that the disciples were not convinced, absolutely persuaded, that the demon would come out. They were afraid.

Why could Jesus not do any miracles in His hometown (Mark 6:5)? Because of their lack of faith.

Justified is a legal term meaning the administration of law and implies that heaven now has legality in the earth realm.

1. We must be fully persuaded and be in agreement in our hearts with what heaven says; this is called faith.

The heart can be fully persuaded of what heaven says, but nothing happens until a man or woman who is in faith releases the authority in the earth realm by speaking it.

The laws of the Kingdom work every time for anyone who will take the time to learn them and apply them.

God had given you everything you would ever need in life through Jesus Christ, who through His sacrifice gave you access to ALL that heaven has.

First John 5:14-15 speak of law, and law gives us confidence of obtaining justice, what is legally ours, because God hears us—He takes the case.

Matthew 6:7-13 teach us how to pray.

Kirsten's Pomeranian puppy showing up was a direct result of the Kingdom and the laws that govern it. The Kingdom produced just like it will every time for anyone who has faith and releases Kingdom authority here in the earth realm.

Chapter Four

The Kingdom of God can impact every area of your life, but you're the one who has to release the provision that you need or want into your life. It won't just happen by itself.

1. Nothing is too small or unimportant to bring under the dominion of the Kingdom.

Chapter Five

Second Peter 1:3a tells you that God's divine power has given you everything you need for life and godliness.

1. It was her choice to be healed that day.

   So many people think they're "waiting" for God to do something in their lives. But God doesn't randomly choose to heal one person one day and not someone else. He's already given ALL of us access to healing through our legal standing in His Kingdom.

2. Her faith allowed her to tap into the power of the Kingdom and receive her healing.

Look at Romans 4:18-21:

> *Against all hope, Abraham in hope believed and so became the father of many nations, just as it had been said to him, "So shall your offspring be." Without weakening in his faith, he faced the fact that his body was as good as dead—since he was about a hundred years old—and that Sarah's womb was also dead. Yet he did not waver through unbelief regarding the promise of God, but was strengthened in his faith and gave glory to God, being fully persuaded that God had power to do what he had promised.*

Faith is being in agreement with heaven, not just mentally but fully persuaded, your heart settled and convinced totally of what God has said, in spite of the natural realm indicating something else.

The principle of man's jurisdiction over the earth is vital to your understanding of Kingdom law.

Abraham is called the father of our faith because he is the man that opened the door of the earth realm to God whereby all nations on the earth would be blessed.

Abraham's faith opened a legal doorway for heaven, which God locked permanently open by making a legal agreement (covenant) with Abraham and his seed, or heirs.

Although Abraham's heirs had the legal agreement available to them, they each still had to fulfill the legal requirement of their own heart, being fully persuaded of what God said, to actually enjoy the personal benefits of the agreement that God and Abraham had made.

Mark 4 tells us in three parables:

The Parable of the Man Scattering Seed

The seed is the Word of God, and the ground is the heart of man or the spirit of man.

Jesus is saying a man scatters the Word of God into his own heart. Then all by itself the soil, or the heart, of man starts to produce faith (agreement with heaven) in the earth realm.

In the natural realm, when the seed in the head is mature, it will look exactly like the seed that was sown into the ground.

There is a supernatural assurance of what heaven says when faith is there.

Faith isn't a product of heaven; it's a product of your heart.

What is the only way you can get faith?
The only way to get faith is by putting the Word of God in your heart and letting the process of agreement take place. Scatter the Word of God into your heart, and let it grow until faith is there.

When the harvest of your faith is available, what must you do?

When the harvest of your faith is available, you must put in the sickle.

What is the "sickle"? Your words

Mastering the formula of saying the right thing isn't the key by itself, as Mark 11:23 shows us:

> *I tell you the truth, if anyone says to this mountain, "Go, throw yourself into the sea," and does not doubt in his heart but believes that what he says will happen, it will be done for him.*

The test of faith is if you believe what you are saying.

Chapter Six

- God created man and put everything under his dominion.
- Man ruled the earth from a position of delegated authority and wore the crown of the government he represented—God's Kingdom.
- Satan, who had already been cast to earth, hated man and lusted after the authority he possessed.
- Adam and Eve lost their legal position of authority in God's Kingdom when they chose to believe Satan and disobey God. They essentially kicked God out.
- This decision had tremendous ramifications on the earth and on every man and woman who would ever live.

  Adam's own painful toil and sweat would be required for the earth to produce what he needed for survival. I call this the earth curse system of survival.

  David calls it the valley of the shadow of death in Psalm 23:4.

Running with painful toil and sweat is the only system we know, but everyone dreams of escaping.

You will never discover your created purpose until you fix the money thing.

Provision is pro-vision.

Chapter Seven

> *Then he will say to those on his left, "Depart from me, you who are cursed, into the eternal fire prepared for the devil and his angels."*
>
> —Matthew 25:41

To rescue man from this fate, God had to reestablish His government's authority in the earth.

What was the only way this could happen?

Someone who wasn't guilty of sin would have to volunteer in Adam's place to take the punishment of death. It would require God to actually place a man on the earth that was not from Adam's lineage who would be willing to sacrifice himself on man's behalf. That man would have to be born here, but not be of the lineage of Adam.

For God's plan to work and to prove the legality of that plan in the earth realm to Satan, who would surely cry foul, God would need to find a man and woman who would believe Him for a child when it was totally and permanently impossible for them to ever have a child.

They would have to believe God to do the impossible.

Why MUST the lineage of Jesus be recorded at the beginning of Matthew?

It is establishing the fact that here in the earth realm Jesus was a descendant of Abraham. This had to be recorded here in the earth where Satan claims his legal dominion and authority. If this list is not accurate or Jesus did not actually come through the lineage of Abraham, then Satan could claim that Jesus's birth and life were a fraud and He was not qualified to pay the price for our sin.

God is NOT a hard taskmaster. He wants to establish your finances.

> *The Lord will send a blessing on your barns and on everything you put your hand to. The Lord your God will bless you in the land he is giving you. The Lord will establish you as his holy people, as he promised you on oath, if you keep the commands of the Lord your God and walk in his ways. Then all the peoples on earth will see that you are called by the name of the Lord, and they will fear you. The Lord will grant you abundant prosperity—in the fruit of your womb, the young of your livestock and the crops of your ground—in the land he swore to your forefathers to give you.*
>
> *The Lord will open the heavens, the storehouse of his bounty, to send rain on your land in season and to bless all the work of your hands. You will lend to many nations but will borrow from none. The Lord will make you the head, not the tail. If you pay attention to the commands of the Lord your God that I give you this day and carefully follow them, you will always be at the top, never at the bottom.*

Chapter Eight

What does Genesis 39:2a, "*The Lord was with Joseph and he prospered*" mean? Isn't the Lord with everyone?

No. Only those in covenant, with legal standing.

Ephesians 2:12 tells us that without a covenant people are without hope and without God in the world.

This legal covenant, allowing God's blessing and influence, overrode the earth realm's painful toil and sweat system. It was legal for God to bless Joseph.

Potiphar's stuff—his estate—and property changed kingdoms.

When Potiphar placed his estate under the jurisdiction of Joseph's authority, he was also placing it under the influence of the blessing of God.

The Sabbath day was a picture of the day when man would no longer have to strive with his own painful toil and sweat just to survive.

The Sabbath was only made possible by the double portion.

The double portion is simply having more than enough, or having something *abundantly* supplied.

Potiphar brought his problems and worries under the jurisdiction of the Kingdom of God, aligning himself with God, and changing allegiance.

Chapter Nine

If you filter every idea through the how-fast-can-I-run filter, you will never tap into the Kingdom way of living, because God is not tied to that system.

If you want to engage the Kingdom, you have to start thinking Kingdom thoughts—ALL things are possible!

When you don't have provision, your vision dies.

What steps did Jesus take?

1. **Sow a portion of whatever it is that you need.**

   Money is a barter system. You and I "name" money every day. Money becomes whatever we need.

2. **Put it under the authority of the Kingdom of God.**

Chapter Ten

By having what you need in life, you are able to labor in the Kingdom, being about your Father's business and your purpose.

In Matthew 17, Peter asked Jesus about paying their taxes.

In verse 27, Jesus simply told Peter where the provision was, the method he needed to use to harvest it, and exactly what he should be looking for. All Peter had to do was go gather it.

God wants to be first in your life.

If money is your treasure, it will be first, demanding your time, your priorities, and your affection.

This is why God has to train you to gather.

What does "seek the Kingdom of God" mean?

It means to find out how it works! Study the laws that govern it. Learn how God's system works.

Chapter Eleven

With God, all things are possible if you'll allow God's Word to change your thinking.

> *Do not conform to the pattern of this world, but be transformed by the renewing of your mind. Then you will be able to test and approve what God's will is—his good, pleasing and perfect will.*
>
> —Romans 12:2

Paul is referring to the earth curse system and how you think.

Jesus came to take your yoke, the painful toil and sweat required by the earth curse system, from you.

You can take His yoke (it is already finished) and find rest (the seventh day, the true Sabbath) for your soul.